The Gamma Function

Athena Series

SELECTED TOPICS IN MATHEMATICS

Edwin Hewitt, *Editor*

Translated by

Michael Butler

The Gamma Function

Emil Artin

**Professor of Mathematics
Hamburg University**

HOLT, RINEHART AND WINSTON

New York • Chicago • San Francisco
Toronto • London

The German original,
"Einführung in die Theorie der Gammafunktion,"
appeared in the
Hamburger Mathematische Einzelschriften
1. Heft/1931, published by Verlag B. G. Teubner, Leipzig

English Translation

Copyright © 1964 by

Holt, Rinehart and Winston, Inc.

Library of Congress Catalog Card Number: 64-22994

20526-0114

Printed in the United States of America

Editor's Preface

A generation has passed since the late Emil Artin's little classic on the gamma function appeared in the *Hamburger Mathematische Einzelschriften*. Since that time, it has been read with joy and fascination by many thousands of mathematicians and students of mathematics. In the United States (and presumably elsewhere as well), it has for many years been hard to find, and dog-eared copies and crude photocopies have been passed from hand to hand. Professor Artin's monograph has given many a student his first look at genuine analysis—the delicacy of its arguments, the precision of its results. Artin had a deep feeling for these aspects of analysis, and he treated them with a master's hand. His undergraduate lectures in the calculus, for example, were filled with elegant constructions and theorems which, alas, Artin never had time to put into printed form. We may be all the more grateful for this beautiful essay, and for its appearance in a new English edition. Various changes made by Artin himself have been incorporated in the present edition. In particular a small error following formula (59) (this edition) was corrected on the basis of a suggestion by Professor Børge Jessen.

Finally, thanks are due to the translator, Mr. Michael Butler, and to the firm of B. G. Teubner for English-language rights.

EDWIN HEWITT

Seattle, Washington
May, 1964

Preface

I have written this monograph with the hope of filling in a certain gap which has often been felt to exist in the mathematical literature. Despite the importance of the gamma function in many different parts of mathematics, calculus books often treat this function in a very sketchy and complicated fashion. I feel that this monograph will help to show that the gamma function can be thought of as one of the elementary functions, and that all of its basic properties can be established using elementary methods of the calculus.

As far as prerequisites are concerned, the reader need only be well acquainted, with calculus, including improper integrals. Some of the more important concepts needed will even be introduced and discussed again in the first chapter. With this background the reader should have no trouble understanding everything but the later parts of the last two chapters, which do assume some knowledge of Fourier series. But then, these parts of the monograph can be passed over on a first reading without any difficulty whatsoever.

The following parts of the theory will *not* be discussed:

(1) Extension to complex variables. For those familiar with the theory of complex variables, it will suffice to point out that for the most part the expressions used are analytic, and hence they retain their validity in the complex case because of the principle of analytic continuation. The only parts of the theory that really need to be changed are those dealing with approximations. This certainly should not be much of an obstacle.

(2) Hölder's theorem showing that the gamma function does not satisfy any algebraic differential equation.

(3) Kummer's series and the integral representation of $\log \Gamma(x)$.

(4) The formula for the logarithmic derivative of $\Gamma(x)$. All the necessary expressions for this can easily be worked out by the reader.

I have chosen the integral as my original definition of the gamma function because this approach saves us the trouble of proving the convergence of Gauss' product. Any other analytic expression having the characteristic properties of the gamma function could just as well have been used. The whole theory will then be deduced using the concept of log convexity. This method comes from Bohr and Mollerup.[1]

EMIL ARTIN

---

[1] H. Bohr and J. Mollerup, *Laerebog i matematisk Analyse* (Kopenhagen 1922), vol. III, 149-164.

Contents

[1]

Convex Functions

Let $f(x)$ be a real-valued function defined on an open interval $a < x < b$ of the real line. For each pair x_1, x_2 of distinct numbers in the interval we form the difference quotient

$$\varphi(x_1, x_2) = \frac{f(x_1) - f(x_2)}{x_1 - x_2} = \varphi(x_2, x_1), \tag{1.1}$$

and for each triple of distinct numbers x_1, x_2, x_3 the quotient

$$\Psi(x_1, x_2, x_3) = \frac{\varphi(x_1, x_3) - \varphi(x_2, x_3)}{x_1 - x_2}$$

$$= \frac{(x_3 - x_2) f(x_1) + (x_1 - x_3) f(x_2) + (x_2 - x_1) f(x_3)}{(x_1 - x_2)(x_2 - x_3)(x_3 - x_1)}. \tag{1.2}$$

The value of the function $\Psi(x_1, x_2, x_3)$ does not change when the arguments x_1, x_2, x_3 are permuted.

$f(x)$ is called *convex* (on the interval (a, b)) if, for every number x_3 of our interval, $\varphi(x_1, x_3)$ is a monotonically increasing function of x_1. This means, of course, that for any pair of numbers $x_1 > x_2$ distinct from x_3 the inequality $\varphi(x_1, x_3) \geqslant \varphi(x_2, x_3)$ holds; in other words, that $\Psi(x_1, x_2, x_3) \geqslant 0$. Since the value of Ψ is not changed by permuting the arguments, the convexity of $f(x)$ is equivalent to the inequality

$$\Psi(x_1, x_2, x_3) \geqslant 0 \tag{1.3}$$

for all triples of distinct numbers in our interval.

Suppose $g(x)$ is another function that is defined and convex on the same interval. By adding (1.3) to the corresponding inequality for $g(x)$, we can easily see that the sum $f(x) + g(x)$ is also convex. More generally, suppose $f_1(x)$, $f_2(x)$, $f_3(x) \cdots$ is a sequence of functions that are all defined and convex on the same interval. Furthermore, suppose that the limit $\lim_{n \to \infty} f_n(x) = f(x)$ exists and is finite for all x in the interval. By forming the inequality (1.3) for $f_n(x)$ with arbitrary but fixed numbers x_1, x_2, x_3, and then taking the limit as $n \to \infty$, we see that $f(x)$ is likewise convex. This proves the following theorem:

1

Theorem 1.1

The sum of convex functions is again convex. The limit function of a convergent sequence of convex functions is convex. A convergent infinite series whose terms are all convex has a convex sum.

The last statement of this theorem follows from the fact that each partial sum of the series is a convex function and the sum of the series is merely the limit of these partial sums.

We are now going to investigate some important properties of a function $f(x)$ defined and convex on the open interval (a, b). For a fixed x_0 in the interval let x_1 range over all numbers $> x_0$ and x_2 range over all numbers $< x_0$. We have

$$\varphi(x_1, x_0) \geqslant \varphi(x_2, x_0). \tag{1.4}$$

If x_2 is kept fixed and x_1 decreases approaching x_0, the left side of Eq. (1.4) will decrease but always remain greater than the right side. This implies that the "right-handed" derivative of $f(x)$ exists; that is to say, the limit

$$\lim_{\substack{x_1 > x_0 \\ x_1 \to x_0^+}} \varphi(x_1, x_0) = \lim_{\substack{x_1 > x_0 \\ x_1 \to x_0^+}} \frac{f(x_1) - f(x_0)}{x_1 - x_0},$$

for which we shall use the intuitive notation $f'(x_0 + 0)$. Furthermore, the inequality (1.4) also shows that

$$f'(x_0 + 0) \geqslant \varphi(x_2, x_0).$$

If we let x_2 increase, approaching x_0, we see that the "left-handed" derivative $f'(x_0 - 0)$ also exists, and that

$$f'(x_0 + 0) \geqslant f'(x_0 - 0). \tag{1.5}$$

Given two numbers $x_0 < x_1$ in our interval, we can choose x_2, x_3 such that $x_0 < x_2 < x_3 < x_1$. Then

$$\varphi(x_2, x_0) \leqslant \varphi(x_3, x_0) = \varphi(x_0, x_3) \leqslant \varphi(x_1, x_3) = \varphi(x_3, x_1).$$

If we let x_2 approach x_0 and x_3 approach x_1, we obtain

$$f'(x_0 + 0) \leqslant f'(x_1 - 0) \quad \text{for} \quad x_0 < x_1. \tag{1.6}$$

This proves that the one-sided derivatives of a convex function always exist and that they satisfy the inequalities (1.5) and (1.6). We shall refer to the properties (1.5) and (1.6) by saying that the one-sided derivatives are monotonically increasing.

In order to show the converse, we must generalize the ordinary mean-value theorem to cover the case of functions for which only the one-sided derivatives exist. The analogue to Rolle's theorem is the following:

Theorem 1.2

Let $f(x)$ be a function, defined and continuous on $a \leqslant x \leqslant b$, whose one-sided derivatives exist in the open interval $a < x < b$. Suppose $f(a) = f(b)$. Then there exists a value ξ with $a < \xi < b$ such that one of the values $f'(\xi + 0)$ and $f'(\xi - 0)$ is $\geqslant 0$ and the other $\leqslant 0$.

Proof

(1) If $f(x)$ takes on its maximum ξ in the interior of our interval, then

$$\frac{f(\xi + h) - f(\xi)}{h}$$

is $\leqslant 0$ for positive h, $\geqslant 0$ for negative h. Taking limits, we get $f'(\xi + 0) \leqslant 0$, $f'(\xi - 0) \geqslant 0$.

(2) If the minimum ξ is taken on in the interior, we obtain similarly $f'(\xi + 0) \geqslant 0$, $f'(\xi - 0) \leqslant 0$.

(3) If both maximum and minimum are at a or b, then $f(x)$ is constant, $f'(x) = 0$, and ξ can be taken anywhere in the interior. This completes the proof.

The substitute for the mean-value theorem is the following:

Theorem 1.3

Let $f(x)$ be defined and continuous on $a \leqslant x \leqslant b$ and have one-sided derivatives in the interior. Then there exists a value ξ in the interior such that $(f(b) - f(a))/(b - a)$ lies between $f'(\xi - 0)$ and $f'(\xi + 0)$.

Proof

The function

$$F(x) = f(x) - \frac{f(b) - f(a)}{b - a}(x - a)$$

is continuous, has one-sided derivatives

$$F'(x \pm 0) = f'(x \pm 0) - \frac{f(b) - f(a)}{b - a},$$

and $F(a) = f(a)$, $F(b) = f(a)$. According to our extension of Rolle's theorem, there is a ξ in the interior such that one of the values

$$f'(\xi + 0) - \frac{f(b) - f(a)}{b - a} \qquad \text{or} \qquad f'(\xi - 0) - \frac{f(b) - f(a)}{b - a}$$

is $\geqslant 0$, the other $\leqslant 0$. This completes the proof.

We are now in a position to prove the desired converse. Let $f(x)$ be a function defined on the open interval $a < x < b$. Suppose $f(x)$ has one-sided derivatives that are monotonically increasing. We contend that $f(x)$ is convex.

Let x_1, x_2, x_3 be distinct numbers in our interval. Since the value of Ψ does not change under permutation of the subscripts, we may assume that $x_2 < x_3 < x_1$. According to the mean-value theorem, we can find ξ, η with $x_2 < \eta < x_3 < \xi < x_1$ such that $\varphi(x_1, x_3)$ lies between $f'(\xi - 0)$ and $f'(\xi + 0)$, and $\varphi(x_2, x_3)$ between $f'(\eta - 0)$ and $f'(\eta + 0)$. Therefore (1.5) implies that

$$\varphi(x_1, x_3) \geqslant f'(\xi - 0) \quad \text{and} \quad \varphi(x_2, x_3) \leqslant f'(\eta + 0).$$

From Eq. (1.2) we obtain

$$\Psi(x_1, x_2, x_3) \geqslant \frac{f'(\xi - 0) - f'(\eta + 0)}{x_1 - x_2}.$$

Finally we conclude from (1.6) that

$$\Psi(x_1, x_2, x_3) \geqslant 0,$$

and this is the contention.

Theorem 1.4

$f(x)$ is an convex function if, and only if, $f(x)$ has monotonically increasing one-sided derivatives.

Corollary

Let $f(x)$ be a twice differentiable function. Then $f(x)$ is convex if, and only if, $f''(x) \geqslant 0$ for all x of our interval.

Proof

$f'(x)$ is monotonically increasing if, and only if, $f''(x) \geqslant 0$.

We now return to Eq. (1.2) and select for x_3 the midpoint $(x_1 + x_2)/2$ of x_1 and x_2. Assuming for a moment that $x_2 < x_1$, we have

$$x_3 - x_2 = x_1 - x_3 = \tfrac{1}{2}(x_1 - x_2).$$

The numerator of $\Psi(x_1, x_2, x_3)$ becomes

$$(x_1 - x_2)\,(\tfrac{1}{2}f(x_1) + \tfrac{1}{2}f(x_2) - f(x_3)),$$

and the denominator is positive. For a convex function we obtain the inequality

$$f\left(\frac{x_1 + x_2}{2}\right) \leqslant \tfrac{1}{2}(f(x_1) + f(x_2)), \tag{1.7}$$

which is symmetric in x_1 and x_2 and therefore also holds for $x_1 < x_2$. For $x_1 = x_2$ it is trival.

We shall call a function defined on an interval *weakly convex* if it satisfies the inequality (1.7) for all x_1, x_2 of the interval. It is obvious that the sum of two weakly convex functions, both defined on the same interval, is again weakly convex. It is also obvious that the limit function of a sequence of weakly convex functions, all defined on the same interval, is weakly convex.

Let $f(x)$ be weakly convex. The inequality (1.7) can be generalized to

$$f\left(\frac{x_1 + x_2 + \cdots + x_n}{n}\right) \leqslant \frac{1}{n}\left(f(x_1) + f(x_2) + \cdots + f(x_n)\right). \qquad (1.8)$$

Proof

(1) We first show that if (1.8) holds for a certain integer n, then it also holds for $2n$. Indeed, suppose x_1, x_2, $\cdots$, x_{2n} are numbers in our interval. Replacing x_1 and x_2 in Eq. (1.7) by

$$\frac{x_1 + \cdots + x_n}{n} \qquad \text{and} \qquad \frac{x_{n+1} + \cdots + x_{2n}}{n},$$

respectively, we have

$$f\left(\frac{x_1 + \cdots + x_{2n}}{2n}\right) \leqslant \tfrac{1}{2}\left(f\left(\frac{x_1 + \cdots + x_n}{n}\right) + f\left(\frac{x_{n+1} + \cdots + x_{2n}}{n}\right)\right).$$

Applying the inequality (1.8) to both terms on the right-hand side, we get the desired formula

$$f\left(\frac{x_1 + \cdots + x_{2n}}{2n}\right) \leqslant \frac{1}{2n}\left(f(x_1) + f(x_2) + \cdots + f(x_{2n})\right).$$

(2) Next we show that if (1.8) holds for $n + 1$, then it also holds for n. With n numbers $(x_1, x_2, \cdots, x_n)$ the number

$$x_{n+1} = \frac{1}{n}(x_1 + \cdots + x_n)$$

also belongs to our interval. If (1.8) holds for $n + 1$, then

$$f(x_{n+1}) = f\left(\frac{nx_{n+1} + x_{n+1}}{n + 1}\right) = f\left(\frac{x_1 + \cdots + x_n + x_{n+1}}{n + 1}\right)$$

$$\leqslant \frac{1}{n + 1}\left(f(x_1) + \cdots + f(x_n) + f(x_{n+1})\right).$$

Transposing the term $1/(n + 1)\, f(x_{n+1})$ to the left side, we obtain (1.8) for the n given numbers.

(3)   We now combine steps (1) and (2) to attain the desired result. If (1.8) holds for any integer n, then step (2) implies that it also holds for all smaller integers. Because of step (1) the contention is true for arbitrarily large integers. Therefore it must be true for all n. This completes the proof.

We wish to prove the following theorem:

Theorem 1.5

A function is convex if, and only if, it is continuous and weakly convex.

Proof

(1)   A convex function is continuous since it has one-sided derivatives. It is also weakly convex, as has already been shown.

(2)   Suppose that $f(x)$ is weakly convex, that there are $x_2 < x_1$ numbers in our interval, and that $0 \leqslant p \leqslant n$ are two arbitrary integers. Apply (1.8) to the case where p of the n numbers have the value x_1 and the remaining $n - p$ numbers have the value x_2. We obtain

$$f\left(\frac{p}{n} x_1 + \left(1 - \frac{p}{n}\right) x_2\right) \leqslant \frac{p}{n} f(x_1) + \left(1 - \frac{p}{n}\right) f(x_2). \qquad (1.9)$$

Assume now that $f(x)$ is continuous and let t be any real number such that $0 \leqslant t \leqslant 1$. Select a sequence of rational numbers between 0 and 1 that converges to t. Every term of this sequence is of the form p/n for suitable integers p and n; therefore Eq. (1.9) can be applied. Since $f(x)$ is continuous, we can go to the limit. We obtain

$$f(tx_1 + (1 - t) x_2) \leqslant tf(x_1) + (1 - t)f(x_2). \qquad (1.10)$$

For any distinct numbers (x_1, x_2, x_3) in our interval we must show that $\psi(x_1, x_2, x_3) \geqslant 0$. Since ψ is symmetric, we may assume that $x_2 < x_3 < x_1$. The denominator of Eq. (1.2) is positive.
We set $t = (x_3 - x_2)/(x_1 - x_2)$; then

$$0 < t < 1, \qquad 1 - t = \frac{x_1 - x_3}{x_1 - x_2}$$

and

$$tx_1 + (1 - t) x_2 = \frac{(x_3 - x_2) x_1 + (x_1 - x_3) x_2}{x_1 - x_2} = x_3 .$$

Hence Eq. (1.10) implies that

$$f(x_3) \leqslant \frac{x_3 - x_2}{x_1 - x_2} f(x_1) + \frac{x_1 - x_3}{x_1 - x_2} f(x_2),$$

which shows that the numerator of ψ is $\geqslant 0$. This completes the proof.

Numerous inequalities useful in analysis can be obtained from Eq. (1.8) by a suitable choice for $f(x)$. As an example, consider $f(x) = -\log x$ for $x > 0$. We have $f''(x) = 1/x^2$ and our function is convex. Therefore Eq. (1.8) implies that

$$-\log \left(\frac{x_1 + \cdots + x_n}{n}\right) \leqslant -\frac{1}{n}(\log x_1 + \log x_2 + \cdots + \log x_n),$$

hence

$$\log \left(\frac{x_1 + \cdots + x_n}{n}\right) \geqslant \log \sqrt[n]{x_1 + \cdots + x_n},$$

and consequently

$$\sqrt[n]{x_1 + \cdots + x_n} \leqslant \frac{x_1 + \cdots + x_n}{n}.$$

We now introduce an important concept closely related to that of convexity. A function $f(x)$ defined and positive on a certain interval is called *log convex* (*weakly log convex*) if the function $\log f(x)$ is convex (weakly convex). The condition that $f(x)$ be positive is obviously necessary, for otherwise the function $\log f(x)$ could not be formed. As an immediate consequence of our previous results, we have the following:

Theorem 1.6

A product of log-convex (weakly log-convex) functions is again log convex (weakly log convex). A convergent sequence of log-convex weakly log-convex) functions has a log-convex (weakly log-convex) limit function, provided the limit is positive.

Instead of the condition that the limit function be positive, we could require that the sequence of the logarithms of the individual terms be convergent.

Theorem 1.7

Suppose $f(x)$ is a twice differentiable function. If the inequalities

$$f(x) > 0, \qquad f(x)f''(x) - (f'(x))^2 \geqslant 0$$

hold, then $f(x)$ is log convex.

This theorem follows directly from the fact that the second derivative of $\log f(x)$ has the value

$$\frac{f(x)f''(x) - (f'(x))^2}{(f(x))^2}.$$

The properties of log-convex functions mentioned thus far are all more or less immediate consequences of the definition. The following remarkable theorem, however, is a much deeper result:

Theorem 1.8

Suppose $f(x)$ and $g(x)$ are functions, defined on a common interval. If both are weakly log convex, then their sum $f(x) + g(x)$ is also weakly log convex. If both are log convex, then $f(x) + g(x)$ is log convex.

Proof

It suffices to prove the first statement. The second then follows immediately with the addition of continuity.

Both $f(x)$ and $g(x)$ are positive. If x_1, x_2 are numbers in our interval, then

$$\left(f\left(\frac{x_1 + x_2}{2}\right)\right)^2 \leqslant f(x_1) f(x_2) \qquad \text{and} \qquad \left(g\left(\frac{x_1 + x_2}{2}\right)\right)^2 \leqslant g(x_1) g(x_2).$$

We have to show that

$$\left(f\left(\frac{x_1 + x_2}{2}\right) + g\left(\frac{x_1 + x_2}{2}\right)\right)^2 \leqslant (f(x_1) + g(x_1)) (f(x_2) + g(x_2)).$$

In other words the proof of our theorem amounts to showing that if a_1, b_1, c_1, a_2, b_2, c_2 are positive real numbers with $a_1 c_1 - b_1^2 \geqslant 0$ and $a_2 c_2 - b_2^2 \geqslant 0$, then

$$(a_1 + a_2) (c_1 + c_2) - (b_1 + b_2)^2 \geqslant 0.$$

Consider the quadratic form $a_1 x^2 + 2 b_1 xy + c_1 y^2$ where $a_1 > 0$. We have

$$a_1(a_1 x^2 + 2 b_1 xy + c_1 y^2) = (a_1 x + b_1 y)^2 + (a_1 c_1 - b_1^2) y^2.$$

If $a_1 c_1 - b_1^2 \geqslant 0$, the quadratic form never takes on a negative value, whatever x, y may be. On the other hand, if $a_1 c_1 - b_1^2 < 0$, the quadratic form takes on the negative value $a_1 c_1 - b_1^2$ for $y = 1$, $x = -(b_1/a_1)$.

Our conditions imply that neither

$$a_1 x^2 + 2 b_1 xy + c_1 y^2 \qquad \text{nor} \qquad a_2 x^2 + 2 b_2 xy + c_2 y^2$$

takes on negative values. Therefore

$$(a_1 + a_2) x^2 + 2(b_1 + b_2) xy + (c_1 + c_2) y^2$$

will not take on negative values. Consequently

$$(a_1 + a_2) (c_1 + c_2) - (b_1 + b_2)^2 \geqslant 0.$$

This completes the proof of the theorem.

The reader who enjoys working with identities can check the validity of the following, for an alternate proof:

$$a_1 a_2 ((a_1 + a_2)(c_1 + c_2) - (b_1 + b_2)^2)$$

$$= a_2(a_1 + a_2)(a_1 c_1 - b_1^2) + a_1(a_1 + a_2)(a_2 c_2 - b_2^2) + (a_1 b_2 - a_2 b_1)^2.$$

If

$$a_1 > 0, \qquad a_2 > 0, \qquad a_1 c_1 - b_1^2 \geqslant 0, \qquad \text{and} \qquad a_2 c_2 - b_2^2 \geqslant 0,$$

the right side is $\geqslant 0$ and the conclusion follows.

Other important facts can be obtained by combining our previous results. Suppose $f(t, x)$ is a function of the two variables x and t, which is defined and continuous for t in the interval $a \leqslant t \leqslant b$ and x in some arbitrary interval. Furthermore, for any fixed value of t, suppose that $f(t, x)$ is a log-convex, twice differentiable function of x. For every integer n we can build the function

$$F_n(x) = h(f(a, x) + f(a + h, x) + f(a + 2h, x) + \cdots + f(a + (n-1)h, x)),$$

where $h = (b - a)/n$. Being the sum of log-convex functions, $F_n(x)$ is also log convex. As n approaches infinity, the functions $F_n(x)$ converge to the integral

$$\int_a^b f(t, x)\, dt;$$

hence this integral is also log convex.

Suppose that $f(t, x)$ only satisfies our conditions in the interior of the t interval, or that the upper bound of the interval is infinite. If the improper integral

$$\int_a^b f(t, x)\, dt$$

exists, then it is log convex. This follows directly from the fact that an improper integral is the limit of proper integrals over subintervals. Hence, as the limit function of log-convex functions, it is also log convex.

In this book we will only have to test integrals of the form

$$\int_a^b \varphi(t)\, t^{x-1}\, dt$$

for log convexity, where $\varphi(t)$ is a positive continuous function in the interior of the integration interval. If we take the logarithm of the integrand and then differentiate twice with respect to x, we get 0.

Theorem 1.9

If $\varphi(t)$ is a positive continuous function defined on the interior of the integration interval, then

$$\int_a^b \varphi(t)\, t^{x-1}\, dt$$

is a log-convex function of x for every interval on which the proper or improper integral exists.

as is always increasing

The following theorem is quite obvious:

Theorem 1.10

If $f(x)$ is log convex on a certain interval, and if c is any real number $\neq 0$, then both the functions $f(x + c)$ and $f(cx)$ are log convex on the corresponding intervals.

[2]

The Euler Integrals and the Gauss Product Formula

The theory of the gamma function was developed in connection with the problem of generalizing the factorial function of the natural numbers, that is, the problem of finding an expression that has the value $n!$ for positive integers n, and that can be extended to arbitrary real numbers at the same time. In looking for such an expression, we come upon the following well-known improper integral:

$$\int_0^\infty e^{-t} t^n \, dt = n!$$

This suggests replacing the integer n on the left side by an arbitrary real number (provided the integral still converges) and defining $x!$ for arbitrary x as the value of this integral. Rather than doing precisely that, we will follow the custom of introducing a function that has the value $(n-1)!$ for positive integers n. Namely,

$$\Gamma(x) = \int_0^\infty e^{-t} t^{x-1} \, dt. \tag{2.1}$$

We still must determine the values of x for which this integral converges. The integrand is smaller than t^{x-1} when t is positive; therefore

$$\int_\epsilon^1 e^{-t} t^{x-1} \, dt < \int_\epsilon^1 t^{x-1} \, dt = \frac{1}{x} - \frac{\epsilon^x}{x}.$$

For $x > 0$,

$$\int_\epsilon^1 e^{-t} t^{x-1} \, dt$$

is bounded from above by $1/x$. If we hold x fixed and let ϵ decrease, the value of the integral increases monotonically. This means that

$$\int_0^1 e^{-t} t^{x-1} \, dt = \lim_{\epsilon \to 0} \int_\epsilon^1 e^{-t} t^{x-1} \, dt$$

exists for all positive x.

11

When t is positive, every term of the series for e^t is positive, and the inequality $e^t > t^n/n!$ holds for all integers n. Hence $e^{-t} < n!/t^n$, which gives another inequality for the integrand, namely, $e^{-t}t^{x-1} < n!/t^{n+1-x}$. Therefore, by holding x fixed and choosing $n > x + 1$, we can make $n!/(n-x)$ an upper bound for

$$\int_1^\delta e^{-t}\,t^{x-1}\,dt.$$

But the value of this integral increases as δ increases, and thus

$$\int_1^\infty e^{-t}\,t^{x-1}\,dt = \lim_{\delta\to\infty}\int_1^\delta e^{-t}\,t^{x-1}\,dt$$

exists. This implies that our definition, Eq. (2.1), is meaningful for all positive real x.

If we replace x by $x + 1$ in Eq. (2.1) and integrate the approximating integral by parts, we get

$$\int_\epsilon^\delta e^{-t}\,t^x\,dt = -\,e^{-t}\,t^x\,\Big|_\epsilon^\delta + x\int_\epsilon^\delta e^{-t}\,t^{x-1}\,dt$$

$$= e^{-\epsilon}\epsilon^x - e^{-\delta}\delta^x + x\int_\epsilon^\delta e^{-t}\,t^{x-1}\,dt.$$

The term $e^{-\delta}\delta^x$ is again smaller than $n!/\delta^{n-x}$. As ϵ approaches 0 and δ approaches $+\infty$, the first two terms on the right side vanish, and we have the formula

$$\Gamma(x+1) = x\Gamma(x). \qquad (2.2)$$

This functional equation is basic for the development of the rest of the theory. It represents a generalization of the identity $n! = n(n-1)!$ for nonintegral values of n. Suppose the value of the gamma function is known on the interval $0 < x \leqslant 1$. With the help of Eq. (2.2) we can easily calculate its value on the interval $1 < x \leqslant 2$, then again on the next interval of length 1, and so on. By repeated application of Eq. (2.2), we get

$$\Gamma(x+n) = (x+n-1)\,(x+n-2)\cdots(x+1)\,x\Gamma(x) \qquad (2.3)$$

for every positive integer n.

Equation (2.1) is only a definition for positive x. Now we want to extend this definition to include negative real numbers. If x lies in the interval $-n < x < -n + 1$, we define the value of the gamma function at x by

$$\Gamma(x) = \frac{1}{x(x+1)\cdots(x+n-1)}\,\Gamma(x+n). \qquad (2.4)$$

If x is a negative integer or 0, the right side of Eq. (2.4) is meaningless. We will consider $\Gamma(x)$ as undefined for these particular numbers. Otherwise, the left side of Eq. (2.4) is well defined, since the argument $(x + n)$ on the right lies in the interval 0 to 1. This extended definition is obviously so constructed that the functional equation, Eq. (2.2), always holds.

The two paragraphs above clearly show that Eq. (2.2) does not determine the gamma function uniquely. If $f(x)$ is any arbitrary function defined on the interval $0 < x \leqslant 1$, we can set

$$f(x + n) = (x + n - 1)(x + n - 2) \cdots (x + 1)\, xf(x) \qquad (2.5)$$

for $0 < x \leqslant 1$, and

$$f(x) = \frac{1}{x(x + 1) \cdots (x + n - 1)} f(x + n)$$

for $-n < x < -n + 1$. Thus $f(x)$ is defined for all real numbers, with the exception of 0 and the negative integers, in such a way that the functional equation $f(x + 1) = xf(x)$ always holds. This certainly makes our definitions, Eqs. (2.1) and (2.4), seem rather arbitrary. If we keep our original problem in mind, it is quite natural to want Eq. (2.2) to hold. It is the appropriate generalization of an elementary property of the factorial function. But an infinite number of arbitrary functions can be found that share this property with the gamma function. What singles out $\Gamma(x)$ from all the other possible functions we could have defined? One glance at the integral in Eq. (2.1) shows that

$$\Gamma(1) = 1,$$

and therefore

$$\Gamma(n) = (n - 1)!. \qquad (2.6)$$

Furthermore, $\Gamma(x)$ is continuous and differentiable. (This will be proved later on.) But even so, an infinite number of other functions that also have these properties can be found.

Our integral in Eq. (2.1), however, has another property that catches the eye. It is log convex. This fact follows immediately from our conclusions concerning integrals and log convexity in Chapter 1. Intuitively, it means that the curve $y = \log \Gamma(x)$ is very smooth. Strange as it may seem, this property is enough to single out $\Gamma(x)$ from all the other solutions of the functional equation $f(x + 1) = xf(x)$.

We shall now prove the following:

An easy calculation gives the inequality

$$f(x) \frac{n}{x+n} \leqslant \frac{n^x n!}{x(x+1) \cdots (x+n)} \leqslant f(x).$$

As n approaches infinity, we get

$$f(x) = \lim_{n \to \infty} \frac{n^x n!}{x(x+1) \cdots (x+n)}.$$

But $\Gamma(x)$ is also a function that satisfies our three conditions. Hence the relation we have just derived is still valid if we put $\Gamma(x)$ instead of $f(x)$ on the left side. This completes the proof of the theorem.

As a corollary we have the formula

$$\Gamma(x) = \lim_{n \to \infty} \frac{n^x n!}{x(x+1) \cdots (x+n)}. \tag{2.7}$$

Actually Eq. (2.7) was only proved for the interval $0 < x \leqslant 1$. To show that it holds in general, we denote the function under the limit sign by $\Gamma_n(x)$. It is easy to see that

$$\Gamma_n(x+1) = x\Gamma_n(x) \frac{n}{x+n+1}, \qquad \Gamma_n(x) = \frac{1}{x} \frac{x+n+1}{n} \Gamma_n(x+1).$$

These two expressions help clarify the following fact: As n approaches infinity, if the limit in Eq. (2.7) exists for a number x, it also exists for $x+1$. Conversely, if it exists for $x+1$ and $x \neq 0$, it also exists for x. Hence the limit exists for exactly those values of x for which $\Gamma(x)$ is defined. If we denote the limit in Eq. (2.7) by $f(x)$, we get the equation $f(x+1) = xf(x)$. Since $f(x)$ already agrees with $\Gamma(x)$ on the interval $0 < x \leqslant 1$, it must also agree everywhere else. Equation (2.7) was derived by Gauss, and it is often used as the fundamental definition of the gamma function.

Another form of Eq. (2.7) which is important in the theory of functions was derived by Weierstrass. A simple manipulation shows that

$$\Gamma_n(x) = e^{x(\log n - 1/1 - 1/2 - \ldots - 1/n)} \frac{1}{x} \frac{e^{x/1}}{1 + x/1} \frac{e^{x/2}}{1 + x/2} \cdots \frac{e^{x/n}}{1 + x/n}.$$

But the limit

$$C = \lim_{n \to \infty} \left(\frac{1}{1} + \frac{1}{2} + \cdots + \frac{1}{n} - \log n \right)$$

exists.* It is often called Euler's constant. Therefore, we have

$$\Gamma(x) = e^{-Cx} \frac{1}{x} \lim_{n\to\infty} \prod_{i=1}^{n} \frac{e^{x/i}}{1 + x/i} = e^{-Cx} \frac{1}{x} \prod_{i=1}^{\infty} \frac{e^{x/i}}{1 + x/i}, \qquad (2.8)$$

where $\prod$ is the product symbol.

We shall now show that the function $\Gamma(x)$ can be differentiated as often as we please; that is, $\Gamma(x)$ has derivatives of arbitrarily high order. Because of the functional equation (2.2), it suffices to prove the assertion for positive x. But $\Gamma(x) > 0$ for $x > 0$, therefore $\log \Gamma(x)$ is defined. From (2.8) we get

$$\log \Gamma(x) = - Cx - \log x + \lim_{n\to\infty} \sum_{i=1}^{n} \left(\frac{x}{i} - \log \left(1 + \frac{x}{i} \right) \right)$$

$$= - Cx - \log x + \sum_{i=1}^{\infty} \left(\frac{x}{i} - \log \left(1 + \frac{x}{i} \right) \right). \qquad (2.9)$$

We will now proceed to prove our assertion for the function $\log \Gamma(x)$. The conclusion for $\Gamma(x)$ will then follow immediately from $\Gamma(x) = e^{\log \Gamma(x)}$. Can we take the derivative of the series in Eq. (2.9) term by term? This can be done if the new series—the one obtained by termwise differentiation—is <u>uniformly</u> convergent. Should this be the case, the left side of Eq. (2.9) is differentiable. The differentiated series obtained from Eq. (2.9) is

$$- C - \frac{1}{x} + \sum_{i=1}^{\infty} \left(\frac{1}{i} - \frac{1}{x + i} \right) = - C - \frac{1}{x} + \sum_{i=1}^{\infty} \frac{x}{i(x + i)}.$$

---

* To prove this we can set

$$C_n = \frac{1}{1} + \frac{1}{2} + \cdots + \frac{1}{n} - \log n \qquad \text{and} \qquad D_n = C_n - \frac{1}{n},$$

which gives us

$$C_{n+1} - C_n = \frac{1}{n + 1} - \log \left(1 + \frac{1}{n} \right),$$

and

$$D_{n+1} - D_n = \frac{1}{n} - \log \left(1 + \frac{1}{n} \right).$$

The elementary inequality

$$\frac{1}{n + 1} < \log \left(1 + \frac{1}{n} \right) < \frac{1}{n}$$

shows that the sequence C_n decreases monotonically, whereas the D_n increases monotonically. Furthermore $D_n < C_n$; hence, $D_1 = 0$ is a lower bound for the C_n. In other words, the sequence C_n converges to a limit.

Because x is positive, the general term of this series is smaller than x/i^2. If we restrict x to an arbitrary interval $0 < x \leqslant r$, then the general term is smaller than r/i^2. This number is completely independent of x. The series

$$\sum_{i=1}^{\infty} \frac{r}{i^2} = r \left(\frac{1}{1^2} + \frac{1}{2^2} + \frac{1}{3^2} + \cdots \right)$$

converges; therefore, our differentiated series converges uniformly. But this means $\log \Gamma(x)$ is differentiable, and that, on the interval in question,

$$\frac{d}{dx} \log \Gamma(x) = \frac{\Gamma'(x)}{\Gamma(x)} = -C - \frac{1}{x} + \sum_{i=1}^{\infty} \left(\frac{1}{i} - \frac{1}{x+i} \right). \qquad (2.10)$$

But the choice of this interval was arbitrary, which implies that Eq. (2.10) holds for all $x > 0$.

Suppose we take the derivative once again. We get the series

$$\frac{1}{x^2} + \sum_{i=1}^{\infty} \frac{1}{(x+i)^2}.$$

The general term is smaller than $1/i^2$ because $x > 0$. This series obviously converges uniformly for positive x. Repeated differentiation leads to ever better converging series, all of which converge uniformly for positive x. This shows that $\log \Gamma(x)$ can be differentiated as often as we please. We have the formula

$$\frac{d^{k-1}}{dx^{k-1}} \left(\frac{\Gamma'(x)}{\Gamma(x)} \right) = \sum_{i=0}^{\infty} \frac{(-1)^k (k-1)}{(x+i)^k}, \qquad k \geqslant 2. \qquad (2.11)$$

There is no trouble in extending the validity of Eq. (2.11) to include negative x. This is easily done with the help of Eq. (2.2). We merely determine the functional equation that the left side of Eq. (2.11) satisfies, and then show that the right side also satisfies it. Both these steps are quite obvious.

The case $k = 2$ is of special interest. The function

$$\frac{d}{dx} \left(\frac{\Gamma'(x)}{\Gamma(x)} \right)$$

is always positive; therefore, the following inequality holds for all x:

$$\Gamma(x) \, \Gamma''(x) - (\Gamma'(x))^2 > 0 \qquad \text{or} \qquad \Gamma(x) \, \Gamma''(x) > (\Gamma'(x))^2 \geqslant 0.$$

This shows that the functions $\Gamma(x)$ and $\Gamma''(x)$ are either both positive or both negative for each particular value of x. Consequently the function $|\Gamma(x)|$ is convex. When is $\Gamma(x)$ positive and when is it negative? We already know that $\Gamma(x)$ is positive for positive x. It follows from Eq. (2.4) that $\Gamma(x)$ has the sign

$(-1)^n$ on the interval $-n < x < -n+1$. Furthermore, Eq. (2.4) shows that $\Gamma(x)$ has a very large absolute value whenever x gets close to zero or a negative integer. If the well-known values of $\Gamma(x)$ for the positive integers are also taken into account, we get a good idea of what the curve $y = \Gamma(x)$ looks like. (The reader is encouraged to draw a sketch.)

The integral of Eq. (2.1) is due to Euler, and it is referred to as *Euler's second integral*. He also discovered another integral related to the gamma function, which is called *Euler's first integral:*

$$B(x, y) = \int_0^1 t^{x-1}(1-t)^{y-1}\, dt. \tag{2.12}$$

This time we have a function of the two variables x and y. We want to prove that the integral exists whenever x and y are positive. First, we write our integral as the sum of two integrals, one from 0 to $\frac{1}{2}$, and the other from $\frac{1}{2}$ to 1. The integrand of the first is always smaller than $t^{x-1}(1-t)^{-1}$ and hence smaller than $2t^{x-1}$. In the second the integrand is always smaller than $t^{-1}(1-t)^{y-1}$ and hence smaller than $2(1-t)^{y-1}$. The method we used to prove the existence of Euler's second integral can now be applied to these two integrals. The rest of the details are left to the reader.

If we replace x by $x+1$ in Eq. (2.12) and write the integral in the form

$$B(x+1, y) = \int_0^1 (1-t)^{x+y-1}\left(\frac{t}{1-t}\right)^x dt,$$

we can integrate by parts. We get

$$\int_\epsilon^{1-\delta} (1-t)^{x+y-1}\left(\frac{t}{1-t}\right)^x dt$$

$$= -\frac{(1-t)^{x+y}}{x+y}\left(\frac{t}{1-t}\right)^x \Big|_\epsilon^{1-\delta} + \int_\epsilon^{1-\delta}\frac{x}{x+y}(1-t)^{x+y}\left(\frac{t}{1-t}\right)^{x-1}\frac{1}{(1-t)^2}\, dt$$

$$= \frac{(1-\epsilon)^y\,\epsilon^x - \delta^y(1-\delta)^x}{x+y} + \frac{x}{x+y}\int_\epsilon^{1-\delta} t^{x-1}(1-t)^{y-1}\, dt.$$

If we let ϵ and δ converge to zero, we get the following functional equation:

$$B(x+1, y) = \frac{x}{x+y}\, B(x, y).$$

Now we hold y fixed and consider the integral of Eq. (2.12) as a function of x. In order to obtain a function that satisfies the functional equation (2.2) we set

$$f(x) = B(x, y)\,\Gamma(x+y).$$

This function obviously satisfies condition (1) in Theorem 2.1. Furthermore, $f(x)$ is the product of two log-convex functions and is therefore log convex

Theorem 2.1

If a function $f(x)$ satisfies the following three conditions, then it is identical in its domain of definition with the gamma function:

(1) $f(x + 1) = xf(x)$.

(2) The domain of definition of $f(x)$ contains all $x > 0$, and is log convex for these x.

(3) $f(1) = 1$.

Proof

The existence of a function with these properties (the gamma function) has already been proved.

Suppose $f(x)$ is a function that satisfies our three conditions. Then Eq. (2.5) is valid because of condition (1), and $f(n) = (n - 1)!$ for all integers $n > 0$ because of condition (3). It suffices to show that $f(x)$ agrees with $\Gamma(x)$ on the interval $0 < x \leqslant 1$. If this is the case, then $f(x)$ must agree with $\Gamma(x)$ everywhere because of condition (1). Let x be a real number, $0 < x \leqslant 1$, and n an integer $\geqslant 2$. The inequality

$$\frac{\log f(-1 + n) - \log f(n)}{(-1 + n) - n} \leqslant \frac{\log f(x + n) - \log f(n)}{(x + n) - n} \leqslant \frac{\log f(1 + n) - \log f(n)}{(1 + n) - n}$$

expresses the monotonic growth of the difference quotient for particular values, and is therefore valid because of condition (2). Since $f(n) = (n - 1)!$, we have

$$\log (n - 1) \leqslant \frac{\log f(x + n) - \log (n - 1)!}{x} \leqslant \log n$$

or

$$\log (n - 1)^x (n - 1)! \leqslant \log f(x + n) \leqslant \log n^x (n - 1)!.$$

But the logarithm is a monotonic function; hence

$$(n - 1)^x (n - 1)! \leqslant f(x + n) \leqslant n^x (n - 1)!.$$

With the help of Eq. (2.5), we get the following inequality for $f(x)$ itself:

$$\frac{(n - 1)^x (n - 1)!}{x(x + 1) \cdots (x + n - 1)} \leqslant f(x) \leqslant \frac{n^x (n - 1)!}{x(x + 1) \cdots (x + n - 1)}$$

$$= \frac{n^x n!}{x(x + 1) \cdots (x + n)} \frac{x + n}{n}.$$

Since this inequality holds for all $n \geqslant 2$, we can replace n by $n + 1$ on the left side. Thus

$$\frac{n^x n!}{x(x + 1) \cdots (x + n)} \leqslant f(x) \leqslant \frac{n^x n!}{x(x + 1) \cdots (x + n)} \frac{x + n}{n}.$$

itself. The log convexity of $B(x, y)$, regarded as a function of x, follows immediately from our theorem on the log convexity of integrals. $\Gamma(x + y)$ is obviously log convex. This means that $f(x)$ also satisfies condition (2) in Theorem 2.1. Condition (3), however, does not hold. We have

$$B(1, y) = \int_0^1 (1 - t)^{y-1} \, dt = \frac{1}{y},$$

and therefore

$$f(1) = \frac{1}{y} \Gamma(1 + y) = \Gamma(y).$$

But this is not really a serious difficulty. Given any function $g(x)$ that satisfies conditions (1) and (2), we can always construct a function that also satisfies (3). Condition (2) implies that $g(1) > 0$, which means we can form the quotient $g(x)/g(1)$. This function satisfies all three conditions and therefore is $\Gamma(x)$. In other words, we have

$$g(x) = g(1) \, \Gamma(x).$$

In our particular case we get

$$f(x) = \Gamma(y) \, \Gamma(x).$$

But this means we have evaluated the integral in Eq. (2.12):

$$\frac{\Gamma(x) \, \Gamma(y)}{\Gamma(x + y)} = \int_0^1 t^{x-1}(1 - t)^{y-1} \, dt. \tag{2.13}$$

This formula holds for all positive x and y.

By setting $x = \frac{1}{2}$ and $y = \frac{1}{2}$ in Eq. (2.13), we get an integral that can easily be evaluated. The substitution $t = \sin^2 \varphi$ gives us

$$(\Gamma(\tfrac{1}{2}))^2 = 2 \int_0^{\pi/2} d\varphi = \pi.$$

But $\Gamma\tfrac{1}{2}$ is positive; therefore, we have the following remarkable and important identity:

$$\Gamma(\tfrac{1}{2}) = \sqrt{\pi}. \tag{2.14}$$

Using Eq. (2.14) and the functional equation (2.1), we can easily calculate the value of $\Gamma(n + \tfrac{1}{2})$ for integral n.

[3]

Large Values of x and the Multiplication Formula

Can we find an elementary function that gives an accurate approximation of $\Gamma(x)$ for large values of x? If the growth of $n!$ is estimated, it is found to increase with n faster than $n^n e^{-n}$, but not quite as fast as $n^{n+1} e^{-n}$.* In other words, the growth of $\Gamma(n)$ is caught between $n^{n-1} e^{-n}$ and $n^n e^{-n}$. This suggests that we consider a function of the form

$$f(x) = x^{x-1/2} e^{-x} e^{\mu(x)}, \tag{3.1}$$

in order to study the behavior of $\Gamma(x)$ for large x. Our goal is to make $f(x)$ satisfy the basic conditions for the gamma function by choosing $\mu(x)$ in an appropriate way.

If we replace x by $x + 1$ in Eq. (3.1) and divide the resulting expression by Eq. (3.1), we get

$$\frac{f(x+1)}{f(x)} = \left(1 + \frac{1}{x}\right)^{x+1/2} x e^{-1} e^{\mu(x+1) - \mu(x)}.$$

This shows that $f(x)$ satisfies condition (1) in Theorem 2.1 if, and only if,

$$\mu(x) - \mu(x+1) = (x + \tfrac{1}{2}) \log\left(1 + \frac{1}{x}\right) - 1, \tag{3.2}$$

holds for $\mu(x)$.

---

* If we consider the elementary inequalities

$$\left(1 + \frac{1}{k}\right)^k < e < \left(1 + \frac{1}{k}\right)^{k+1}$$

for $k = 1, 2, \cdots, (n-1)$, and multiply them together, we get

$$\frac{n^{n-1}}{(n-1)!} < e^{n-1} < \frac{n^n}{(n-1)!}.$$

This leads to the approximation

$$e n^n e^{-n} < n! < e n^{n+1} e^{-n}.$$

20

We denote the right side of Eq. (3.2) by $g(x)$. A function $\mu(x)$ with this property is easy to find. If we set

$$\mu(x) = \sum_{n=0}^{\infty} g(x + n),$$
(3.3)

then Eq. (3.2) holds, provided the infinite series in Eq. (3.3) converges. Let us postpone the proof of convergence for a moment and consider condition (2) of theorem 2.1.

The factor $x^{x-1/2} e^{-x}$ in Eq. (3.1) is log convex because the second derivative of its logarithm, $1/x + \frac{1}{2}x^2$, is always positive when x is positive. If we can show that the factor $e^{\mu(x)}$ is log convex, in other words that $\mu(x)$ is convex, then $f(x)$ also satisfies condition (2). This means that the function $f(x)$ determined by the particular $\mu(x)$ we defined in Eq. (3.3) will agree with $\Gamma(x)$ to within a constant factor. Our $\mu(x)$ is convex if the general term of the series $g(x + n)$ is convex. To show this, it suffices to prove the convexity of $g(x)$ itself. But we have

$$g''(x) = \frac{1}{2x^2(x + 1)^2} > 0.$$

The convergence of the series in Eq. (3.3) still remains to be shown. We will combine this with an approximation of the function $\mu(x)$. Let us begin by considering the expansion

$$\frac{1}{2} \log \frac{1 + y}{1 - y} = \frac{y}{1} + \frac{y^3}{3} + \frac{y^5}{5} + \cdots,$$

which is valid for $|y| < 1$. Now we replace y by $1/(2x + 1)$. The resulting expansion is valid for positive x because $1/(2x + 1) < 1$ whenever $x > 0$. We multiply this equation by $2x + 1$ and bring the first term on the right side over to the left side:

$$(x + \tfrac{1}{2}) \log \left(1 + \frac{1}{x}\right) - 1 = g(x)$$

$$= \frac{1}{3(2x + 1)^2} + \frac{1}{5(2x + 1)^4} + \frac{1}{7(2x + 1)^6} + \cdots.$$

This expression again shows that $g(x)$ is convex, since every term on the right side is convex. Now we can approximate $g(x)$. If the integers 5, 7, 9, $\cdots$ are all replaced by 3, then the value of the right side increases. The result is an infinite geometric series, having $1/(3(2x + 1)^2)$ as its first term and $1/(2x + 1)^2$ as its ratio. Its sum is

$$\frac{1}{3(2x + 1)^2} \frac{1}{1 - (1/(2x + 1)^2)} = \frac{1}{12x(x + 1)} = \frac{1}{12x} - \frac{1}{12(x + 1)}.$$

But $g(x)$ is positive, hence

$$0 < g(x) < \frac{1}{12x} - \frac{1}{12(x+1)} \, .$$

Since every term of the series in Eq. (3.3) is positive, it suffices to show the convergence of

$$\sum_{n=0}^{\infty} \left(\frac{1}{12(x+n)} - \frac{1}{12(x+n+1)} \right),$$

which converges trivially to the limit $1/12x$. This not only proves our assertion, it also gives the approximation

$$0 < \mu(x) < \frac{1}{12x} \, .$$

In other words,

$$\mu(x) = \frac{\theta}{12x}$$

where θ is a number independent of x between 0 and 1.

By a suitable choice of the constant a, we get

$$\Gamma(x) = a x^{x-1/2} \, e^{-x+\mu(x)} = a x^{x-1/2} \, e^{-x+\theta/12x}. \tag{3.4}$$

If we let x be an integer n and multiply the expression by n, we get the approximation

$$n! = a n^{n+1/2} \, e^{-n+\theta/12n}. \tag{3.5}$$

We are now going to find the exact value of this constant a and determine some other important constants at the same time.

Let p be a positive integer. We consider the function

$$f(x) = p^x \Gamma \left(\frac{x}{p} \right) \Gamma \left(\frac{x+1}{p} \right) \cdots \Gamma \left(\frac{x+p-1}{p} \right),$$

for $x > 0$. The second derivative of $\log p^x$ is zero, and each of the functions $\Gamma((x+i)/p)$ is obviously log convex. This implies that $f(x)$ is also log convex. If we replace x by $x + 1$, p^x takes on the factor p, $\Gamma((x+i)/p)$ goes over into the next factor, and $\Gamma((x+p-1)/p)$ becomes

$$\Gamma \left(\frac{x}{p} + 1 \right) = \frac{x}{p} \Gamma \left(\frac{x}{p} \right) \, .$$

In other words, $f(x)$ is multiplied by x. Our function again satisfies the conditions (1) and (2) in Theorem 2.1; therefore,

$$p^x \Gamma \left(\frac{x}{p} \right) \Gamma \left(\frac{x+1}{p} \right) \cdots \Gamma \left(\frac{x+p-1}{p} \right) = a_p \Gamma(x), \tag{3.6}$$

where a_p is a constant depending on p. For $x = 1$ in Eq. (3.6), we have

$$a_p = p\Gamma\left(\frac{1}{p}\right) \Gamma\left(\frac{2}{p}\right) \cdots \Gamma\left(\frac{p}{p}\right). \tag{3.7}$$

If we set $x = k/p$ in Eq. (2.7), then a simple manipulation gives

$$\Gamma\left(\frac{k}{p}\right) = \lim_{n\to\infty} \frac{n^{k/p} n! \, p^{n+1}}{k(k+p)(k+2p)\cdots(k+np)}.$$

Now we set $k = 1, 2, \cdots, p$, one after the other, and multiply all these expressions together. Factors of the form $(k + hp)$ appear in the denominator, where k runs from 1 to p, and h runs from 0 to n. For $h = 0$ we get the numbers from 1 to p; for $h = 1$, the numbers from $p + 1$ to $2p$; and so on. The product in the denominator is obviously $(np + p)!$. The final result is

$$a_p = p \lim_{n\to\infty} \frac{n^{(p+1)/2} (n!)^p \, p^{np+1}}{(np + p)!}.$$

The well-known infinite product

$$1 = \lim_{n\to\infty} \left(1 + \frac{1}{np}\right)\left(1 + \frac{2}{np}\right) \cdots \left(1 + \frac{p}{np}\right),$$

which can be written as

$$1 = \lim_{n\to\infty} \frac{(np + p)!}{(np)! \, (np)^p},$$

can now be applied. If we multiply this last expression with the above identity for a_p, we obtain

$$a_p = p \lim_{n\to\infty} \frac{(n!)^p \, p^{np}}{(np)! \, n^{(p-1)/2}}.$$

But Eq. (3.5) implies that

$$(n!)^p = a^p n^{np+p/2} \, e^{-np} \, e^{\theta_1 p/12n},$$

$$(np)! = a(np)^{np+1/2} \, e^{-np} \, e^{\theta_2/12np}.$$

After making the appropriate substitutions above, we obtain

$$a_p = \sqrt{p} \; a^{p-1} \lim_{n\to\infty} e^{(\theta_1 p/12n) - (\theta_2/12np)},$$

and finally

$$a_p = \sqrt{p} \; a^{p-1}. \tag{3.8}$$

By evaluating a_2 with the help of Eq. (3.7) and then comparing the result with Eq. (3.8), we get

$$a_2 = 2\Gamma(\tfrac{1}{2})\,\Gamma(1) = 2\,\sqrt{\pi} = a\,\sqrt{2}.$$

But this determines the exact values of our constants:

$$a = \sqrt{2\pi} \qquad \text{and} \qquad a_p = p^{1/2}(2\pi)^{(p-1)/2}.$$

Now we gather together all the important expressions from this chapter:

$$\Gamma(x) = \sqrt{2\pi}\; x^{x-1/2}\, e^{-x+\mu(x)},$$

$$\mu(x) = \sum_{n=0}^{\infty} (x + n + \tfrac{1}{2}) \log \left(1 + \frac{1}{x+n}\right) - 1 = \frac{\theta}{12x}, \qquad 0 < \theta < 1,$$

$$n! = \sqrt{2\pi}\; n^{n+1/2}\, e^{-n+\theta/12n}. \quad \text{could } \theta = \gamma ? \tag{3.9}$$

$$\Gamma\left(\frac{x}{p}\right) \Gamma\left(\frac{x+1}{p}\right) \cdots \Gamma\left(\frac{x+p-1}{p}\right) = \frac{(2\pi)^{(p-1)/2}}{p^{x-1/2}}\, \Gamma(x). \tag{3.10}$$

In particular, for $p = 2$

$$\Gamma\left(\frac{x}{2}\right) \Gamma\left(\frac{x+1}{2}\right) = \frac{\sqrt{\pi}}{2^{x-1}}\, \Gamma(x). \tag{3.11}$$

The formulas in Eq. (3.9), which describe the behavior of $\Gamma(x)$ for large values of x, are called *Stirling's formulas*. If our approximation of $\mu(x)$ is used, the accuracy of the formula for $\Gamma(x)$ will increase as x increases. This is also true for estimates of $n!$ The relative accuracy for $n \geqslant 10$ is already quite high.

The functional equation (3.10), discovered by Gauss, is called *Gauss' multiplication formula*. By replacing x by px in Eq. (3.10), we obtain an expression for $\Gamma(px)$ as the product of factors, each of the form $\Gamma(x + (k/p))$. This fact gave rise to the name "multiplication formula." The most important special case is $p = 2$. It was discovered by Legendre and is often referred to as *Legendre's relation*.

The Connection with sin x

The gamma function satisfies another very important functional equation. In order to derive it, we set

$$\varphi(x) = \Gamma(x)\,\Gamma(1-x)\,\sin \pi x. \tag{4.1}$$

This function is only defined for nonintegral arguments. If we replace x by $x + 1$, then $\Gamma(x)$ becomes $x\Gamma(x)$. The function $\Gamma(1 - x)$ becomes

$$\Gamma(-x) = \frac{\Gamma(1-x)}{-x},$$

and $\sin \pi x$ changes its sign. This means that $\varphi(x)$ is left fixed, and is therefore periodic of period 1:

$$\varphi(x + 1) = \varphi(x). \tag{4.2}$$

The Legendre relation can be written in the form

$$\Gamma\left(\frac{x}{2}\right) \Gamma\left(\frac{x+1}{2}\right) = b 2^{-x}\, \Gamma(x),$$

where b is a constant. Actually, the exact value of b was determined in Chapter 3. But this extra information need not (and will not) be assumed here. As far as we are concerned now, b is just some particular constant.

In the expression above, we replace x by $1 - x$:

$$\Gamma\left(\frac{1-x}{2}\right) \Gamma\left(1 - \frac{x}{2}\right) = b 2^{x-1}\, \Gamma(1-x).$$

Now we consider

$$\varphi\left(\frac{x}{2}\right) \varphi\left(\frac{x+1}{2}\right) = \Gamma\left(\frac{x}{2}\right) \Gamma\left(1 - \frac{x}{2}\right) \sin \frac{\pi x}{2} \, \Gamma\left(\frac{x+1}{2}\right) \Gamma\left(\frac{1-x}{2}\right) \cos \frac{\pi x}{2}$$

$$= \frac{b^2}{4}\, \Gamma(x)\, \Gamma(1-x)\, \sin \pi x,$$

and we get the relation

$$\varphi\left(\frac{x}{2}\right) \varphi\left(\frac{x+1}{2}\right) = d\varphi(x), \tag{4.3}$$

where d is a constant depending on b. The exact value of d is not important here.

Since both $\Gamma(x)$ and $\sin x$ can be differentiated as often as we please, $\varphi(x)$ also has this property. Because of the functional equation (2.2), we can write

$$\varphi(x) = \frac{\Gamma(1 + x)}{x} \Gamma(1 - x) \sin \pi x$$

$$= \Gamma(1 + x)\, \Gamma(1 - x) \left(\pi - \frac{\pi^3 x^2}{3!} + \frac{\pi^5 x^4}{5!} - \cdots \right),$$

where the power series converges for all values of x. But the right side of this equation is also defined for $x = 0$, and it represents a function having derivatives of all orders at this point. This suggests that we extend our definition, Eq. (4.1), by giving $\varphi(x)$ the value π at $x = 0$. Because our function is periodic, we define π to be the value of $\varphi(x)$ for all integral arguments. $\varphi(x)$ is now continuous everywhere and has derivatives of all orders at every point. The relation of Eq. (4.3) was only proven for nonintegral x. But if we let x approach an arbitrary integer, the validity of Eq. (4.3) for all x follows from continuity. As far as the sign of $\varphi(x)$ is concerned, Eq. (4.1) shows that $\varphi(x)$ is positive on the interval $0 < x < 1$. Because of Eq. (4.2), this is now true for all x.

Our goal is to prove that $\varphi(x)$ is a constant. Let $g(x)$ denote the second derivative of $\log \varphi(x)$. $g(x)$ is also periodic of period 1. Because of Eq. (4.3), it satisfies the functional equation

$$\tfrac{1}{4}\left(g\left(\frac{x}{2}\right) + g\left(\frac{x+1}{2}\right) \right) = g(x). \tag{4.4}$$

Since $g(x)$ is continuous on the interval $0 \leqslant x \leqslant 1$, it is bounded on this interval, say, $|g(x)| \leqslant M$. But this inequality holds for all x, because $g(x)$ is periodic.

The following argument shows that $g(x)$ vanishes. Equation (4.4) gives us the inequality

$$|g(x)| \leqslant \tfrac{1}{4}\left| g\left(\frac{x}{2}\right)\right| + \tfrac{1}{4}\left| g\left(\frac{x+1}{2}\right)\right| \leqslant \frac{M}{4} + \frac{M}{4} = \frac{M}{2}.$$

This means that the upper bound can be pushed down from M to $M/2$. If we repeat the process again, we get $M/4$ as an upper bound, and so on. In other words, the upper bound for $g(x)$ can be made as small as we please. This implies that $g(x) = 0$. But $g(x)$ was the second derivative of $\log \varphi(x)$, hence $\log \varphi(x)$ is a linear function. Furthermore, $\log \varphi(x)$ is periodic, which means that $\log \varphi(x)$ must be a constant. Therefore $\varphi(x)$ is also a constant. We already know one value of $\varphi(x)$, namely, $\varphi(0) = \pi$. This implies that $\varphi(x) = \pi$ for all x.

Recalling the definition of $\varphi(x)$ in Eq. (4.1), we get

$$\Gamma(x)\, \Gamma(1 - x) = \frac{\pi}{\sin \pi x}, \tag{4.5}$$

which is often called *Euler's functional equation*. If we set $x = \frac{1}{2}$ in Eq. (4.5), we get a new proof of Eq. (2.14). The exact value of the constant in Legendre's relation was never used; therefore, this proof of Eq. (2.14) is independent of what was done in Chapter 3.

With the help of Eq. (2.2) we can write Eq. (4.5) in the form

$$\sin \pi x = \frac{\pi}{- x \Gamma(x)\, \Gamma(- x)}.$$

Now we substitute the expressions for $\Gamma(x)$ and $\Gamma(- x)$ given by Weierstrass' product formula, Eq. (2.8). This gives the following representation of $\sin \pi x$ as an infinite product:

$$\sin \pi x = \pi x \prod_{i=1}^{\infty} \left(1 - \frac{x^2}{i^2}\right). \tag{4.6}$$

If we had assumed this product development of $\sin \pi x$ to start with (there are other proofs for the expression), we could have derived Eq. (4.5) by direct calculation. The approach we took is preferable, inasmuch as it gives us Eq. (4.6) at the same time. For the importance of Eq. (4.6) in analysis, we refer the reader to books on function theory.

Let us formulate the main result of this section as a theorem:

Theorem 4.1

Every positive periodic function that has a continuous second derivative and satisfies the functional equation (4.3) is a constant.

[5]

Applications to Definite Integrals

There is extensive literature that deals with more-or-less trivial manipulations of the two Euler integrals. We can only mention a few of the important results here.

If we set $e^{-t} = \tau$ in Eq. (2.1), and then write t instead of τ again, we get

$$\Gamma(x) = \int_0^1 \left(\log \frac{1}{t}\right)^{x-1} dt. \tag{5.1}$$

Similarly, the substitution $t^x = \tau$ turns Eq. (2.1) into

$$\Gamma(x) = \int_0^\infty e^{-t^{1/x}} \frac{1}{x} dt.$$

If we replace x by $1/x$, then

$$\Gamma\left(1 + \frac{1}{x}\right) = \int_0^\infty e^{-t^x} dt. \tag{5.2}$$

The case $x = 2$ in Eq. (5.2) is of special interest:

$$\int_0^\infty e^{-t^2} dt = \tfrac{1}{2}\sqrt{\pi}. \tag{5.3}$$

The number of similar manipulations can be extended indefinitely. We will mention one other example of importance in analytic number theory. If $a > 0$, the substitution $t = a\tau$ leads to the integral

$$\frac{\Gamma(x)}{a^x} = \int_0^\infty e^{-at} t^{x-1} dt. \tag{5.4}$$

Now we turn our attention to the first Euler integral, Eq. (2.13). The substitutions $t = \tau/(\tau + 1)$ and $\sin^2 \varphi$, respectively, give the expressions

$$\int_0^\infty \frac{t^{x-1}}{(1 + t)^{x+y}} dt = \frac{\Gamma(x)\,\Gamma(y)}{\Gamma(x + y)}, \tag{5.5}$$

and

$$\int_0^{\pi/2} (\sin \varphi)^{2x-1} (\cos \varphi)^{2y-1} d\varphi = \tfrac{1}{2} \frac{\Gamma(x)\,\Gamma(y)}{\Gamma(x + y)}. \tag{5.6}$$

If we set $y = (1 - x)$ in Eq. (2.13), Eq. (4.5) gives us the following interesting special cases:

$$\int_0^1 t^{x-1}(1 - t)^{-x}\, dt = \frac{\pi}{\sin \pi x}, \qquad 0 < x < 1, \tag{5.7}$$

$$\int_0^\infty \frac{t^{x-1}}{1 + t}\, dt = \frac{\pi}{\sin \pi x}, \qquad 0 < x < 1, \tag{5.8}$$

$$2 \int_0^{\pi/2} (\operatorname{tg} \varphi)^{2x-1}\, d\varphi = \frac{\pi}{\sin \pi x}, \qquad 0 < x < 1. \tag{5.9}$$

If x and y are both rational numbers, Eq. (2.13) is the intergal of an algebraic function. Suppose we set $x = m/n$ and $y = \frac{1}{2}$ in Eq. (2.13), and make the substitution $t = \tau^n$. We get

$$\int_0^1 \frac{t^{m-1}}{\sqrt{1 - t^n}}\, dt = \frac{\Gamma(m/n)\, \sqrt{\pi}}{n\Gamma(m/n + 1/2)}. \tag{5.10}$$

For $m = 1$ and $n = 4$ or $n = 3$, we get the following numerical results, with the help of Eqs. (3.11) and (4.5):

$$\int_0^1 \frac{dt}{\sqrt{1 - t^4}} = \frac{(\Gamma(1/4))^2}{\sqrt{32\pi}}, \tag{5.11}$$

$$\int_0^1 \frac{dt}{\sqrt{1 - t^3}} = \frac{(\Gamma(1/3))^3}{\sqrt{3}\ \sqrt[3]{16\pi}}, \tag{5.12}$$

which shows a connection between these particular numbers and the elliptical integrals.

An integral representation for the error $\mu(x)$ in Stirling's formula can also be found. Since we have

$$\int_0^1 \frac{1/2 - t}{t + x}\, dt = (x + \tfrac{1}{2}) \log \left(1 + \frac{1}{x}\right) - 1,$$

the series in Eq. (3.9) can be written in the form

$$\mu(x) = \sum_{n=0}^\infty \int_0^1 \frac{1/2 - t}{t + n + x}\, dt.$$

If we define the following noncontinuous function:

$$H(t) = \begin{cases} \tfrac{1}{2} - t, & \text{for} \quad 0 < t < 1 \\ 0, & \text{for} \quad t = 0 \\ \text{otherwise periodic of period 1} \end{cases}$$

it follows that

$$\mu(x) = \sum_{n=0}^{\infty} \int_0^1 \frac{H(t)}{t+n+x} \, dt = \sum_{n=0}^{\infty} \int_n^{n+1} \frac{H(t)}{t+x} \, dt = \lim_{n \to \infty} \int_0^n \frac{H(t)}{t+x} \, dt.$$

Because the integrand is an oscillating function that approaches zero as t approaches infinity, the integral

$$\mu(x) = \int_0^{\infty} \frac{H(t)}{t+x} \, dt \qquad (5.13)$$

exists.

Equation (5.13) is the first step in deriving the so-called *Stirling series,* a refinement of Stirling's formula. We now introduce the functions

$$H_{2n}(t) = 2 \, (-1)^{n-1} \sum_{i=1}^{\infty} \frac{\cos 2i\pi t}{(2i\pi)^{2n}} \, ,$$

$$H_{2n-1}(t) = 2 \, (-1)^n \sum_{i=1}^{\infty} \frac{\sin 2i\pi t}{(2i\pi)^{2n-1}} \, . \qquad (5.14)$$

We know that $-H_1(t) = H(t)$, because $-H_1(t)$ is the Fourier series for $H(t)$. For $n \geqslant 2$, the series $H_n(t)$ is absolutely and uniformly convergent for all x; for $n = 1$, the series converges uniformly in every closed interval that contains no integer. Therefore Eq. (5.14) implies that

$$H'_{n+1}(t) = H_n(t). \qquad (5.15)$$

When $n \geqslant 2$, this holds for all x; when $n = 1$, for all nonintegral x. Because $H_{n+1}(t)$ is always continuous, Eq. (5.15) implies that

$$\int_0^t H_n(t) \, dt = H_{n+1}(t) - H_{n+1}(0). \qquad (5.16)$$

The functions $H_n(t)$ are periodic of period 1, so it suffices to study them on the interval $0 \leqslant t < 1$. Because $H_1(t)$ is a polynomial on this interval, $H_n(t)$ must also be a polynomial there. We maintain that the coefficients of these polynomials are all rational numbers. This can be shown by induction. Our assertion is true when $n = 1$; we assume that it also holds for $H_n(t)$. This implies that

$$\int_0^t H_n(t) \, dt,$$

is a rational polynomial; thus it suffices to prove that $H_{n+1}(0)$ is a rational number. When $n + 1$ is odd, Eq. (5.14) implies $H_{n+1}(0) = 0$. When $n + 1$ is even, we can set $H_{n+1}(t) = \varphi(t) + H_{n+1}(0)$, where $\varphi(t)$ is a rational polynomial. If we integrate this expression, then using Eq. (5.16) we get

$$H_{n+2}(t) - H_{n+2}(0) = H_{n+2}(t) = \int_0^t \varphi(t)\, dt + H_{n+1}(0)\, t,$$

because $n + 2$ is odd. But Eq. (5.14) implies that $H_{n+2}(1)$ vanishes; thus we have the expression

$$0 = \int_0^1 \varphi(t)\, dt + H_{n+1}(0), \tag{5.17}$$

which enables us to calculate $H_{n+1}(0)$ and show that it is rational.

We are now in a position to write Eq. (5.13) in the desired form. Repeated integration by parts gives

$$\mu(x) = \frac{H_2(0)}{x} + \frac{H_3(0)\, 1!}{x^2} + \frac{H_4(0)\, 2!}{x^3} + \cdots$$

$$+ \frac{H_n(0)\, (n-2)!}{x^{n-1}} - \int_0^\infty \frac{H_n(t)\, (n-1)!}{(t+x)^n}\, dt. \tag{5.18}$$

An easy calculation shows that the sum of the last two terms in Eq. (5.18) is equal to

$$\int_0^\infty \frac{(H_n(0) - H_n(t))\, (n-1)!}{(t+x)^n}\, dt\,.$$

If n is even, $H_n(0) - H_n(t)$ has the same sign (plus or minus) as $H_n(0)$ for all t; thus the integral above also has this sign. Furthermore, Eq. (5.14) implies that the numbers $H_{2n+1}(0)$ all vanish, and that the signs of the numbers $H_{2n}(0)$ alternate between plus and minus. This shows that the partial sums

$$\frac{H_2(0)\, 0!}{x} + \frac{H_4(0)\, 2!}{x^3} + \cdots + \frac{H_{2n}(0)\, (2n-2)!}{x^{2n-1}}$$

are alternately larger and smaller than $\mu(x)$. In other words, for every n there exists a number θ, $0 < \theta < 1$, so that

$$\mu(x) = \frac{H_2(0)\, 0!}{x} + \frac{H_4(0)\, 2!}{x^3} + \cdots + \frac{H_{2n-2}(0)\, (2n-4)!}{x^{2n-3}}$$

$$+ \theta \frac{H_{2n}(0)\, (2n-2)!}{x^{2n-1}}, \qquad 0 < \theta < 1. \tag{5.19}$$

We can not take the limit in Eq. (5.19) because the series diverges. But so long as n does not get too large, it gives us a very useful approximation. When $n = 8$, for example, we get the approximation

$$\mu(x) = \frac{1}{12x} - \frac{1}{360x^3} + \frac{1}{1260x^5} - \frac{\theta}{1680x^7}\,. \tag{5.10}$$

We now have a method for computing $\Gamma(x)$. In the interval $4 \leqslant x \leqslant 5$, for instance, we can compute $\mu(x)$ to within six decimal places by using Eq. (5.20). The first formula in Eq. (3.9) gives the value of $\log \Gamma(x)$ with the same accuracy. Using the functional equation (2.2), we finally get the value of $\Gamma(x)$ in the interval from 1 to 2. This enables us to compute $\Gamma(x)$ for arbitrary x. When x is very large, Eq. (3.9) can be used directly.

Anyone familiar with the so-called Bernoulli numbers will recognize the connection with our $H_n(0)$. The reader is left to pursue this topic on his own.

[6]

Determining Γ*(x) by Functional Equations*

We have aquainted ourselves with three different functional equations for the gamma function: the functional equation (2.2), the multiplication formula, and Euler's formula. To what extent is the gamma function determined by one, or a combination, of these equations?

Suppose for the time being that $f(x)$ is an arbitrary function and that $\varphi(x)$ denotes the quotient $f(x)/\Gamma(x)$. If $f(x)$ satisfies a functional equation of the type in Eqs. (2.2), (3.10) or (4.5), then $\varphi(x)$ will clearly satisfy the corresponding equation among the following:

$$\varphi(x+1) = \varphi(x), \tag{6.1}$$

$$\varphi\left(\frac{x}{p}\right)\varphi\left(\frac{x+1}{p}\right)\cdots\varphi\left(\frac{x+p-1}{p}\right) = \varphi(x), \tag{6.2}$$

$$\varphi(x)\,\varphi(1-x) = 1. \tag{6.3}$$

If $f(x)$ satisfies Legendre's functional equation (3.11), for instance, then

$$\varphi\left(\frac{x}{2}\right)\varphi\left(\frac{x+1}{2}\right) = \varphi(x). \tag{6.4}$$

For the sake of simplicity, we will assume from now on that $f(x)$ satisfies the functional equation (2.2); consequently, $\varphi(x)$ is periodic of period 1, that is, $\varphi(x)$ satisfies Eq. (6.1). We will also assume that $f(x)$, along with $\varphi(x)$, is continuous for all x. As a result of Eq. (6.1), the continuity of $\varphi(x)$ for positive x implies continuity at zero and at negative integers, provided $\varphi(x)$ is defined for these values in the right way. If Eqs. (6.2) or (6.3) also hold, they are valid for all x because of continuity.

If we assume further that $f(x)$ is always positive when x is positive, then the logarithm of $\varphi(x)$ is continuous. If we denote $\log \varphi(x)$ by $g(x)$, the corresponding functional equations (in addition to $g(x+1) = g(x)$) are

$$g\left(\frac{x}{p}\right) + g\left(\frac{x+1}{p}\right) + \cdots + g\left(\frac{x+p-1}{p}\right) = g(x), \tag{6.5}$$

$$g(x) = -g(1-x) = -g(-x), \tag{6.6}$$

$$g\left(\frac{x}{2}\right) + g\left(\frac{x+1}{2}\right) = g(x). \tag{6.7}$$

33

If $f(x)$ has a continuous second derivative, then so does $\varphi(x)$. We will assume this to be the case, and also that $\varphi(x)$ satisfies Eq. (6.4). But then $\varphi(x)$ must be a constant. This follows from the theorem proven at the end of Chapter 4. Because of Eq. (6.4), the value of this constant must be 1. In other words, we have $f(x) = \Gamma(x)$.

Theorem 6.1

The gamma function is the only solution of both Eq. (2.2) and Eq. (3.11) that is positive for positive x and possesses a continuous second derivative.

This theorem demonstrates the significance of the Legendre functional equation. Our next step is to find out whether the assumption of a continuous second derivative can be weakened. As a matter of fact, we will be able to show that a continuous first derivative is sufficient.

Suppose we start with a preliminary observation. Equation (6.5) represents an infinite number of functional equations, one for each value of p. But these equations are not independent of each other. Assume, for instance, that Eq. (6.5) holds for the integers p_1 and p_2. If we consider it for the integer p_1, but with the argument $(x + k)/p_2$, we get

$$\sum_{i=0}^{p_1-1} g\left(\frac{x + k + ip_2}{p_1 p_2}\right) = g\left(\frac{x + k}{p_2}\right).$$

Now we take the sum over k from zero to $p_2 - 1$. On the right side we get $g(x)$, since Eq. (6.5) holds for p_2. But $k + ip_2$ runs over all integers from zero to $p_1 p_2 - 1$. This yields the equation

$$\sum_{j=0}^{p_1 p_2 - 1} g\left(\frac{x + j}{p_1 p_2}\right) = g(x);$$

therefore Eq. (6.5) also holds for the product $p_1 p_2$.

With this in mind, let us assume that Eq. (6.7) holds. Then Eq. (6.5) is valid for all integers of the form 2^n, and hence for arbitrarily large values of p. More generally, if Eq. (6.5) holds for an integer p, it also holds for the powers of that integer, and hence for certain arbitrarily large integers.

Now we take the derivative of Eq. (6.5)

$$\frac{1}{p}\left(g'\left(\frac{x}{p}\right) + g'\left(\frac{x + 1}{p}\right) + \cdots + g'\left(\frac{x + p - 1}{p}\right)\right) = g'(x), \qquad (6.8)$$

and partition the positive x axis into intervals of length $1/p$, beginning with the origin. The arguments in the left side of Eq. (6.8) fall into p distinct consecutive intervals. Since $g'(x)$ is periodic of period 1, we have a value of the function from each of the intervals between zero and 1. But Eq. (6.8) holds for arbitrarily large values of p. As p approaches infinity, the left side of Eq. (6.8) converges to the integral

$$\int_0^1 g'(x)\, dx = g(1) - g(0) = 0.$$

This means that $g'(x) = 0$ for all x; consequently $g(x)$ is a constant. The value of this constant is zero, as can be seen from any of the equations in (6.5) which happen to hold. This proves the following theorem:

Theorem 6.2

The gamma function is the only continuously differentiable function that is positive for positive values of x, and that satisfies both Eq. (2.2) and Eq. (3.10) for some value of p.

Now we might be tempted to conjecture that continuity alone suffices. This is not true at all. The function

$$g(x) = \sum_{n=1}^{\infty} \frac{1}{2^n} \sin\left(2^n \pi x\right), \tag{6.9}$$

is continuous, because the series converges uniformly. It is also periodic, and it is easy to see that it satisfies Eq. (6.7). But it is not identically equal to zero. It is not even a constant:

$$g(x) = 0, \qquad g(\tfrac{1}{4}) = \tfrac{1}{2}.$$

If we assume mere continuity, what other properties must also be assumed to make Theorem 6.2 valid? Equation (6.6) is not sufficient; the function in Eq. (6.9) also satisfies Eq. (6.6). A finite number of Eq. (6.5) is not sufficient either. Similar counter examples can always be constructed. But what happens if we assume that $g(x)$ satisfies Eq. (6.5) for *all* integers p? As a conclusion to our study of the gamma function it will be shown that this property is sufficient.

In order to do this we will make use of some facts about Fourier series. Let $f(x)$ be an integrable function of period 1. Setting (for any α)

$$c_\nu = \int_0^1 f(x)\, e^{-2\pi i \nu x}\, dx = \int_\alpha^{\alpha+1} f(x)\, e^{-2\pi i \nu x}\, dx,$$

we associate with $f(x)$ the series

$$\sum_{\nu=-\infty}^{+\infty} c_\nu e^{2\pi i \nu x},$$

regardless of whether or not this series converges. We denote this association by

$$f(x) \sim \sum_{\nu=-\infty}^{+\infty} c_\nu e^{2\pi i \nu x}.$$

We see immediately that the Fourier series of a sum of two functions is the sum of the two Fourier series.

The Fourier series of $f(x + \alpha)$ has the coefficients

$$d_\nu = \int_0^1 f(x + \alpha) \, e^{-2\pi i \nu x} \, dx = \int_\alpha^{\alpha+1} f(x) \, e^{-2\pi i \nu (x-\alpha)} \, dx$$

$$= e^{2\pi i \nu \alpha} \int_\alpha^{\alpha+1} f(x) \, e^{-2\pi i \nu x} \, dx;$$

hence $d_\nu = e^{2\pi i \nu \alpha} c_\nu$. We see that the Fourier series of $f(x + \alpha)$ is obtained from that of $f(x)$ by making the substitution $x \to x + \alpha$.

Let $k \geqslant 1$ be an integer. The Fourier coefficient d_ν of the function $f(kx)$ is given by

$$d_\nu = \int_0^1 f(kx) \, e^{-2\pi i \nu x} \, dx = \frac{1}{k} \int_0^k f(x) \, e^{-2\pi i \nu x / k} \, dx$$

$$= \frac{1}{k} \sum_{m=1}^{k} \int_{m-1}^{m} f(x) \, e^{-2\pi i \nu x / k} \, dx = \frac{1}{k} \sum_{m=1}^{k} \int_0^1 f(x) \, e^{-2\pi i \nu (x+m-1/k)} \, dx$$

$$= \frac{1}{k} \left(\sum_{m=1}^{k} e^{-2\pi i \nu (m-1)/k} \right) \int_0^1 f(x) \, e^{-2\pi i \nu x / k} \, dx.$$

The sum in the last expression above is a geometric series with the ratio $e^{-2\pi i \nu / k}$. If $\nu = \mu k$ is divisible by k, each term of the sum is 1, and we obtain

$$d_{\mu k} = \int_0^1 f(x) \, e^{-2\pi i \mu x} \, dx = c_\mu .$$

If ν is not divisible by k, $e^{-2\pi i \nu / k} \neq 1$, and the formula for the sum of the geometric series shows that $d_\nu = 0$. Therefore

$$f(kx) \sim \sum_{\mu=-\infty}^{+\infty} c_\mu e^{2\pi i \nu k x}.$$

The Fourier series for $f(kx)$ is obtained from that of $f(x)$ by merely substituting kx for x.

If $f(x)$ is continuous and the Fourier series converges for a particular value x_0, the value of the Fourier series for $x = x_0$ is the function value $f(x_0)$. The reader will find a proof of this fact in most books on Fourier series. As a matter of fact a consequence of Fejer's theorem is that the Fourier series of a continuous function $f(x)$ is always summable (even if not convergent) to $f(x)$.

We are now in a position to proceed with the proof at hand. Suppose our function $g(x)$ satisfies Eq. (6.5) for all integers p. Replacing x by px, we obtain from Eq. (6.5)

$$g(x) + g\left(x + \frac{1}{p}\right) + \cdots + g\left(x + \frac{p-1}{p}\right) = g(px). \tag{6.10}$$

If we let

$$g(x) \sim \sum_{\nu=-\infty}^{+\infty} c_\nu e^{2\pi i \nu x},$$

then

$$g\left(x + \frac{m}{p}\right) \sim \sum_{\nu=-\infty}^{+\infty} c_\nu e^{2\pi i \nu x} e^{2\pi i \nu m / p},$$

and

$$g(px) \sim \sum_{\nu=-\infty}^{+\infty} c_\nu e^{2\pi i \nu px}. \tag{6.11}$$

Substituting this into Eq. (6.10), we see that

$$\sum_{m=0}^{p-1} \sum_{\nu=-\infty}^{+\infty} c_\nu e^{2\pi i \nu x} e^{2\pi i \nu m / p} = \sum_{\nu=-\infty}^{+\infty} c_\nu e^{2\pi i \nu x} \left(\sum_{m=0}^{p-1} e^{2\pi i \nu m / p} \right)$$

is the Fourier series of the left side.

Just as before, we obtain for

$$\sum_{m=0}^{p-1} e^{2\pi i \nu m / p}$$

the value p if ν is divisible by p and zero if ν is not divisible by p. The Fourier series of $g(px)$ is, consequently,

$$\sum_{\mu=-\infty}^{+\infty} p c_{\mu p} \, e^{2\pi i \mu px}.$$

Comparing this result with Eq. (6.11), we find that

$$c_\mu = p c_{\mu p} \,.$$

In particular for the cases $\mu = 1, -1, 0$

$$c_p = \frac{c_1}{p}; \qquad c_{-p} = \frac{c_{-1}}{p}; \qquad c_0 = 0.$$

Since we have assumed that Eq. (6.5) holds for all integers $p \geqslant 1$, we get

$$g(x) \sim \sum_{\nu=1}^{\infty} \left(\frac{c_1}{\nu} e^{2\nu\pi i x} + \frac{c_{-1}}{\nu} e^{-2\nu\pi i x} \right).$$

But $g(x)$ is a real-valued function, and hence

$$g(x) \sim \sum_{\nu=1}^{\infty} \left(\frac{a}{\nu} \sin 2\nu\pi x + \frac{b}{\nu} \cos 2\nu\pi x \right).$$

The terms

$$\sum_{\nu=1}^{\infty} \frac{\sin 2\nu\pi x}{\nu} \quad \text{and} \quad \sum_{\nu=1}^{\infty} \frac{\cos 2\nu\pi x}{\nu}$$

are the Fourier series for the functions $\pi H(x)$ and $- \log (2 \sin \pi x)$, respectively, where $H(x)$ denotes the function introduced in Chapter 5. Therefore, at every point of continuity,

$$g(x) = a\pi H(x) - b \log (2 \sin \pi x).$$

The function $H(x)$ is bounded, the function $- \log (2 \sin \pi x)$ is not. This implies that $b = 0$ for continuous $g(x)$. But $H(x)$ is not continuous; hence $a = 0$. This proves the following theorem:

Theorem 6.3

The gamma function is the only continuous function that is positive for positive x, and that satisfies Eq. (2.2) and Eqs. (3.10) for all values of p.

Index